This book belongs to

. . . .

Get the most from this reader

Before reading:

● Look at the pictures and discuss them together.
  Ask questions such as, "What is the spider
  sitting on?"

● Discuss what your child thinks will happen in the
  book and why. Check after reading to see if this
  prediction was correct.

● Relate the topic to your child's world. For
  example, say: "Have you seen bees inside
  flowers in our garden?"

During reading:

● Prompt your child to sound out unknown words.
  Draw attention to neglected middle or
  end sounds.

● If your child makes a mistake, ask if the text makes
  sense and allow him or her time to correct it
  before helping.

● Occasionally, ask what might happen next,
  and then check together as you read on.

- Monitor your child's understanding. Repeated readings can improve fluency and comprehension.

- Keep reading sessions short and enjoyable. Stop if your child becomes tired or frustrated.

■ ■

After reading:

- Discuss the book. Encourage your child to form opinions with questions such as, "Did you like the ending? Why or why not?"

- Help your child work through the fun activities at the back of the book. Then ask him or her to reread the story. Praise any improvement.

Worm was feeling sad.
He didn't make anything,
and he didn't help anyone.

"I'm not useful," he said. "All I do is slither in soil. I wish I could work like my friends."

9

Worm went to see his friend Snail. "What is your job, Snail?" asked Worm. "Can I help you?"

"I clean up the garden," said Snail.
"I break up food waste to make compost,
but I don't need any help today."

11

Worm wondered if his friend
Ant needed any help.
"I'm looking for a job," said Worm.
"Can I help you with your work?"

"Sorry, Worm, I can't stop. I need to carry these seeds back to my nest. We will eat some, and some will grow into new plants."

"Hello, Bee!" said Worm.
"Can I work with you?"

"Hi, Worm!" said Bee.
"You need to fly to work with me.
I collect nectar from flowers.
Then, I use the nectar to make
honey. It feeds the baby bees."

"Maybe I can do what Spider does," thought Worm. So, he went to see Spider.
"What are you doing, Spider?" he asked.

"I'm too busy to talk right now," said Spider. "I'm making a web to catch pests."

Worm was unhappy.
"Will I ever find a useful job?"
he asked his friends.

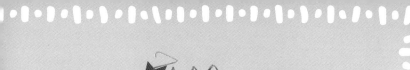

"You already have a useful job," they said. "When you slither along, you mix up the earth. This helps plants grow. You have an important job."

"Wow! I am useful," said Worm.
"I am a hard worker. I think
I need a break."

Discussion Questions

1 Who makes honey?

2 How do ants help us?

3 Do you think worms are important? Why?

❧ Sight Words ❧

Learning sight words helps you read fluently. Practise these sight words from the book. Use them in sentences of your own.

went

could

make

any

what

was

grow

with

Rhyming Words

Can you find the rhyming pairs?
Say them aloud.

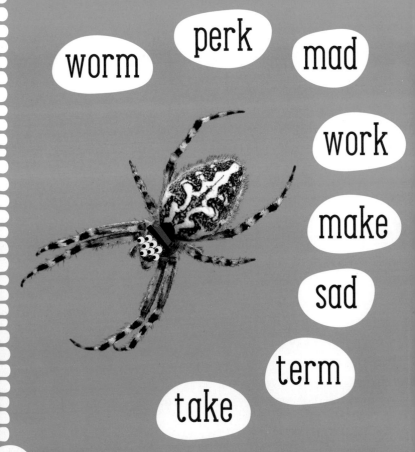

perk

worm

mad

work

make

sad

term

take

25

Writing Practice

Read the words, and then trace them with your finger.

anything

helpful

slither

garden

compost

wonder

important

spider

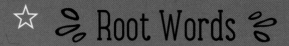

Root Words

Match each word
with its root word.

Root words:

happy
feel
help
go
work
make

Words:

feeling
goes
making
unhappy
helpful
worked

Words for Comparing

Follow the lines to match each word with its comparison and superlative.

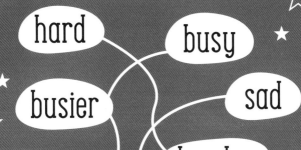

hard

busy

busier

sad

clean

harder

cleaner

hardest

sadder

cleanest

busiest

saddest